HEINEMANN GUIDED READERS
BEGINNER

GU00994828

NORMAN

The Sky's the Limit

BEGINNER LEVEL

Series Editor: John Milne

The Heinemann Guided Readers provide a choice of enjoyable reading material for learners of English. The series is published at five levels – Starter, Beginner, Elementary, Intermediate and Upper. At **Beginner Level**, the control of content and language has the following main features:

Information Control

The stories are written in a fluent and pleasing style with straightforward plots and a restricted number of main characters. The cultural background is made explicit through both words and illustrations. Information which is vital to the story is clearly presented and repeated where necessary.

Structure Control

Special care is taken with sentence length. Most sentences contain only one clause, though compound sentences are used occasionally with the clauses joined by the conjunctions 'and', 'but', and 'or'. The use of these compound sentences gives the text balance and rhythm. The use of Past Simple and Past Continuous Tenses is permitted since these are the basic tenses used in narration and students must become familiar with these as they continue to extend and develop their reading ability.

Vocabulary Control

At **Beginner Level** there is a controlled vocabulary of approximately 600 basic words, so that students with a basic knowledge of English will be able to read with understanding and enjoyment. Help is also given in the form of vivid illustrations which are closely related to the text.

For further information on the full selection of Readers at all five levels in the series, please refer to the Heinemann Readers catalogue.

1

A New Start for Max

Max Price was a happy man. He loved his wife, Angela, and his two children, Stephen and Juliet. Max and his family lived in a small, pleasant flat. They had many good friends and kind neighbours. Yes, the Price family was a happy family!

But one day, Max lost his job. The bad news came in a letter. The letter was short and clear. Max became very worried.

'What shall I do now?' he said to his wife.

'I don't know, Max. I don't know,' replied Angela. She was very worried too.

Then Max became angry.

'Look at this letter,' he said. 'They send me "Best Wishes". I don't want "Best Wishes", I want a job. I've got a wife and family!'

'Don't worry, Max,' said Angela. 'Everything will be all right.'

'But who will give me a job now, Angela? I'm thirty-seven! And today, thirty-seven is old. What are we going to do?'

'Let's ask our friends and neighbours,' said Angela.

But they got no help from their friends and neighbours. Many people were looking for jobs. Life was difficult for everybody.

Every morning, Max looked for a new job. Every afternoon, he came home without one. And every evening, he waited for the newspaper.

' "Friendship Services International". It's a new company,' said Max. 'What do you think, Angela?'

'Go and see them!' said Angela. 'They need new people. Men and women. And all ages, too!'

'Yes,' said Max. 'The Star Building. That's the new skyscraper in the city centre. It's a big company, Angela. Very big!'

'You can go in the morning,' said Angela.

'I will,' said Max. He was excited. 'I'll be there early. I'll be there at seven o'clock. I'll get a job, Angela. Don't worry!'

Early next morning, Max was at the Star Building. At nine o'clock, he had an interview with three men from Friendship Services International.

'What was your last job?' asked Mr Lelais, the personnel manager.

'I sold furniture,' said Max.

'We don't need furniture salesmen here,' said the second man, Mr Creep.

'But I'll learn a new job,' said Max quickly. 'I'll work hard.'

'Good,' said the third man, Mr Hightower. 'We need new men. And we need hard workers, Mr . . .'

'. . . Price,' said Max quickly.

'Very good, Price,' said Mr Hightower. 'Be here tomorrow at eight-thirty. You are now working for Friendship Services International.'

Now Max had a job. He ran home and told Angela the good news. This was a new start for Max!

2

The Ground Floor

The next day, Max went to his new job. His office was on the ground floor of the Star Building. Many new people started work that day. One of them was Frank Steadman. He became Max's friend.

Their office was large and busy, but everybody was very friendly. Max and Frank liked everybody, and they did their work well.

'I like it here, Max,' said Frank one day. 'We've got good jobs at Friendship Services International!'

'Yes,' said Max. 'I like it here too!'

So the two men were very happy. Every lunchtime, they had drinks and sandwiches with their new friends.

In the evenings, they went to parties with them. Max and Frank often took their wives and children to the parties. Max was pleased, and Angela was pleased too.

Max now had a good salary. So he and Angela bought lots of new furniture for their flat. They bought a colour television, a hi-fi, and many other things. Angela bought some new clothes. And the children had lots of new toys. The Price family was happy again.

'You're rich!' said Angela one day to Max.

Max laughed. 'No, not yet Angela,' he said. 'But perhaps I'll be rich one day.'

'Let's drink to your new job,' said Angela.

'Yes,' agreed Max. 'Let's drink to my new employer. Let's drink to Friendship Services International. Cheers, Angela!'

'Cheers, Max,' said Angela.

The work at Friendship Services International was hard. Every day, Max and Frank received lots of letters. These letters wanted 'FSI products'. But FSI products had no names. They only had numbers and letters: X3Ys, L7Ks, A5Qs. What did these strange numbers and letters mean? Max and Frank did not know!

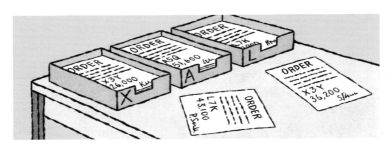

Each day, they opened hundreds of these orders. They put the orders into groups: one group for 'X' products, one group for 'L' products, and one group for 'A' products. The orders came from all over the world. Some of the orders were very big.

'We're working very hard,' said Max to Frank one day.

'Yes,' replied Frank. 'Letters, letters, letters! Hundreds of them! What do they mean, Max? What do they want? What are they asking for?'

'I don't know,' said Max. 'Don't ask so many questions, Frank!'

'OK!' said Frank. 'OK.'

Later that day, a memo came from their boss, Mr B. Creep.

3

The Fifth Floor

Max and Frank now worked on the fifth floor. There were two other men and one secretary in their new office.

The office was quiet. Its furniture was modern and expensive. The secretary had a dictaphone and an electric typewriter. The four men had large desks.

One day, Max and Frank looked down on the street below. There was a lot of noise and traffic in the street. Max and Frank remembered their friends on the ground floor.

'They were good friends,' said Frank.

'Yes,' said Max. 'But now we've got new friends on the fifth floor.'

'But remember the parties and the friendship on the ground floor,' said Frank.

'Yes,' said Max. 'But Frank! The salaries on the fifth floor are better!'

Max now had more money. 'Let's buy a new house,' he said to Angela.

'But I like it here,' said Angela. 'And the children like it here too.'

'But, Angela,' said Max, 'I now work on the fifth floor at Friendship Services International. My salary is bigger. Fifth floor people don't live in flats. They live in houses!'

'But, Max,' said Angela, 'all our friends live here. And the children go to school here. And our flat is lovely now.'

Max became angry. 'We are going to move, Angela. We are going to move next week.'

'All right,' said Angela. She smiled, but she was unhappy.

The next week, Max and Angela moved to a new house. But Frank Steadman and his wife did not move.

'We like our flat,' said Frank. 'All our friends are near us. And the children like their school. No, I shall not move, Max.'

Max said nothing.

Max and Frank worked hard in their fifth floor office. They received orders to Friendship Services International, and priced them.

For example, there was an order for five thousand M5Bs. The prices were in a book. One M5B cost ten dollars. So five thousand M5Bs cost 5000 x 10 = 50 000 dollars. But Max and Frank still did not understand 'M5B'.

'What's an M5B?' asked Frank.

'I don't know,' said Max.

———

Now their boss was Mr M. Hightower. His office was on the tenth floor of the Star Building. He came down every day at five o'clock and spoke to Max and Frank.

'Your work is excellent, gentlemen,' said Mr Hightower one day. 'Excellent!'

'Thank you, Mr Hightower,' said Max.

'Call me Mort, please!' said Mr Hightower.

'Thank you, Mort. I will,' said Max. But Frank said nothing.

One day, Mr Hightower came down early. Max and Frank were alone in their office.

'Anything wrong, Mort? asked Max.

15

4

Higher and Higher

The tenth floor office was large and comfortable. Max and Frank were the only two men in it. They had large desks and large telephones. There was a secretary too. She also had a large desk.

One morning, Max and Frank looked down on the city below. It was a long way! The people and the cars were very small.

'It's very high, Frank,' said Max. 'I like it up here!'

'It's too high, Max,' said Frank. 'I liked it on the ground floor. There's too much work up here.'

'But we must work,' said Max. 'This is Friendship Services International. It's a good company. We must work!'

Max worked very hard. He often worked late in the office.

One evening, Max came home early. Angela was pleased.

'Hello Max! You're early tonight. I'm cooking your favourite meal.'

'I'm sorry, Angela,' said Max. 'I must go out again in a few minutes. I've got an important business dinner.'

'Oh, please stay,' said Angela. 'I don't see you a lot these days. And the children don't see you at all.'

'I'm sorry, Angela,' said Max. 'But it's an important dinner. I must go. Goodbye.'

'Goodbye, Max. Good luck!'

Oh Max, thought Angela to herself. You are becoming a different man. And the children don't know you now. You are a stranger in our home.

It was a very important business dinner. Max and Frank were there. They met many foreign customers of

Friendship Services International. But Mort Hightower wasn't at the dinner.

'Where's Hightower tonight?' asked Frank.

'Mort? I don't know,' said Max. 'He wasn't well this morning. He left the office early.'

Max and Frank talked to the dinner guests. They came from all over the world. They were rich. They ate and drank a lot.

'We like Friendship Services International,' said an African guest.

'Yes, your products are very good,' said an Asian guest.

Then Max asked a question. He spoke to an American guest.

'Excuse me,' he said.

'Yes?' said the American.

'I've read your letters to FSI,' said Max. 'I've seen your orders. For example, you ordered three hundred S6Ts.'

'That's right,' said the American. 'Three hundred S6Ts. They were excellent.'

'But what is "S6T"?' asked Max. 'What do your orders mean? I don't understand them.'

The American laughed. 'Oh! Our orders! Don't worry,' he said. 'You'll learn one day. But not now, Max!' The other guests laughed too.

Max and Frank were going to ask another question. But at that moment, there was an urgent message for Max.

5

An Important Man

The office on the fifteenth floor had every modern office machine. There was also a beautiful carpet on the floor and modern paintings on the walls. Max didn't like the paintings, but they were expensive. That pleased Max.

From the window, Max looked out at the other skyscrapers in the city.

Yes, thought Max, I'm an important man now. I'm rising higher in FSI. I'm rising higher in the Star Building. And I've got a beautiful secretary!

It was true. Max's secretary was called Donna Lot. She was beautiful. She liked Max and Max liked her. They did a lot of work together.

Max and Donna often worked late. Sometimes they went to restaurants after work. One evening, Max telephoned Angela from a restaurant.

'Hello, Angela darling!' he said. 'It's Max here.'

'Max!' said Angela. 'Where are you? We're waiting for you. It's nine o'clock!'

'I'm in the office,' said Max. 'I'm working late.'

'But Max!' said Angela. 'It's Stephen's birthday. He's waiting for you.'

'Oh!' said Max. 'I forgot! I'm sorry, Angela. I'll see him tomorrow.'

'Tomorrow, Max?' said Angela. 'Tomorrow? Oh, Max. Your work is more important to you than your home.'

Angela was angry. She put the phone down. Max rang her again. But Angela did not answer.

Max did not see his son the next day. He went to work early. There were many letters for him. Max and Donna worked hard.

'Do you understand these letters?' Max asked Donna.

'What do you mean, Max?' she replied.

'Do you understand these orders?' said Max. 'What is a B5R? What is a G9Q? Do you know?'

Donna spoke slowly. 'They're secret things,' she said.

'I know!' said Max. 'But why are they secret?'

'I don't know, Max,' said Donna. Then she smiled. 'But you can find out!'

'How?' asked Max. 'How can I find out?'

'You can become a Director of the company,' said Donna.

Max laughed. 'Me? Max Price? A Director of Friendship Services International? It's impossible.'

'It isn't impossible,' said Donna. 'I can help you.'

'You?' said Max. He was surprised. 'How can you help me?'

6

Bad News, Good News!

A few months later, Max became a Director of Friendship Services International. He went to his first board meeting. It was on the twentieth floor of the Star Building. Max did not know the other men there. They were talking about sales and profits.

'X5Bs are selling well,' said one man.

'And we're making good profits on B3Qs,' said another man.

Max looked at his papers. 'C7Ts are selling well,' he said. 'And we're making good profits on U8Ds.'

'Thank you,' said somebody. 'Thank you, Mr Price.'

Everybody smiled at Max. Max smiled at everybody.

But Max still did not understand. 'C7Ts' and 'U8Ds' were selling well! But what were they? Max didn't know.

Now Max was very busy. He always arrived home very late.

One evening, he arrived home about midnight. He was very tired. But Angela and the children were not there. Max looked in all the rooms. There was nobody.

'Angela!' shouted Max. 'Where are you? Stephen! Juliet! Where are you? I'm home! It's Daddy!'

But there was no answer.

Max went into the bedroom again. Then he found a letter. It was on the bed. Max looked at the envelope. Suddenly he felt sad. Suddenly he knew. He opened the envelope and read the letter. Yes, it was from Angela.

Dear Max,
I'm going away with the children. Goodbye. Goodbye of Max. We will think of you. Goodbye.
All my love,
Angela.
P.S. Good luck on the Board of Directors.

Now Max had no family. He was sad and lonely. So he travelled.

He travelled for Friendship Services International. He travelled all over the five continents: Europe, Africa, Asia, America, Australia. Max was very good at his work. His customers liked him.

Max took letters and papers to each customer. Many of the customers were scientists. The papers were "TOP SECRET". Max did not understand them. He was not a scientist.

He showed the papers to customers in many foreign countries. The customers read the documents. Then they made decisions.

For example, one African scientist said, 'Thank you, Mr Price. Thank you for the papers. They are very interesting. I shall order fifteen S3Bs and four hundred M2Gs.'

Soon Max was very popular with the other Directors.

'Excellent work, Max,' said the Finance Director one day.

'Yes, excellent,' said the company's Vice Chairman.

7

The Sky's the Limit!

Now Max was the Chairman of Friendship Services International. Now he was at the top of the Star Building.

His office was on the twenty-fifth floor. It was a very strange office. It was a very large, white room. There was a big desk and one chair.

On the desk there were two telephones. One telephone had the letter 'M' on it. The other telephone had the letter 'W'.

Max said to himself, 'What are these phones for?' But he did not know.

There was a very large window in the office. From the window, Max looked out at the clear blue sky. He

remembered the Friendship Services International advertisement – *The Sky's the Limit!*

He remembered the interview with Mr Lelais, Mr Creep, and Mort Hightower. Then he thought about Frank Steadman.

Where's Frank now? Max thought. But Max did not know.

And Max remembered his wife, Angela, and his children, Stephen and Juliet. They never came back.

Every evening, Max went home to an empty house. But now his beautiful home was dirty. Nobody visited Max. He had no friends. He was alone. He was unhappy.

Every evening, Max wrote a letter. Every letter was the same.

Max put each letter into an envelope. On every envelope Max wrote, 'To my darling Angela'. Now there were nearly a hundred letters. They were all the same.

Max was Chairman of FSI, but he had no work. Every day, he came to his office. But every day, there was no work.

One morning, he found a large book on his desk. 'What's this?' he asked himself.

At that moment, the 'M' telephone rang. Max picked it up. A voice said, 'Send us five hundred N5Bs immediately. You will find details in the catalogue.'

'But who are you?' asked Max. 'And what are N5Bs?'

Max waited, but there was no answer.

The 'W' telephone rang. Max picked it up. Another voice said, 'Send us five hundred N5Bs immediately. You will find details in the catalogue.'

'But who are you?' Max asked again. 'And what are N5Bs?'

Again Max waited, but there was no answer. He was now frightened.

'Who is "M"?' said Max. 'And who is "W"? And N5B? What is N5B?' Max picked up the catalogue on his desk. He opened it at 'N'.

Heinemann English Language Teaching
Halley Court, Jordan Hill, Oxford OX2 8EJ
A division of Reed Educational & Professional Publishing Limited

OXFORD MADRID FLORENCE ATHENS PRAGUE
SÃO PAULO MEXICO CITY CHICAGO PORTSMOUTH(NH)
TOKYO SINGAPORE KUALA LUMPUR MELBOURNE
AUCKLAND JOHANNESBURG IBADAN GABORONE

Heinemann is a registered trademark of Reed Educational & Professional
Publishing Limited

ISBN 0 435 27175 X

© Norman Whitney 1977, 1992
First published 1977
Reprinted five times
This edition published 1992

A recorded version of this story is available on cassette.
ISBN 0 435 27283 7

Illustrated by David Webster
Typography by Adrian Hodgkins
Cover by Jim Mawtus and Threefold Design
Typeset in 12/16 pt Goudy
by Joshua Associates Ltd, Oxford
Printed and bound in Malta by Interprint Limited

97 98 99 00 01 10 9 8 7 6 5